The American
MOTHER GOOSE

The American MOTHER GOOSE

by Ray Wood

With a foreword by
John A. Lomax
Illustrations
by Ed Hargis

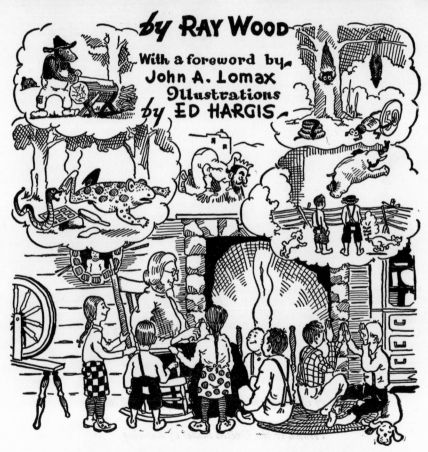

J. B. LIPPINCOTT COMPANY
Philadelphia   New York

Library of Congress catalog card number 40-27623

Printed in the United States of America

INTRODUCTION

"Tipty, tipty up stairs,
Tipty, tipty down stairs;
Fell and broke its backbone
And never could be mended."

How well do I remember the feeling of triumph that came to me when none of my companions could solve this riddle! I never did tell them the answer. I've never told anyone. But such riddles kept alert and alive the young minds of the latter quarter of the twentieth century down in Texas by the Rio Grande. In that time and place they learned by "word of mouth" and not by the written page. Perhaps other children, little and big, may likewise come to love these quaint reminders of other years. Years ago I lived

[v]

in a Texas frontier community that made a perfect setting for the rhymes that Ray Wood has included in the *American Mother Goose*. Soon after the Civil War my father had emigrated with his family from Mississippi to Bosque County, then a Texas border district. Jack and Fan, two big mules, pulled one wagon carrying the family; while Bright and Berry, a span of spotted oxen, dragged a heavier wagon on which were piled the household goods and gods. Six hundred miles and three months of travel, over a winding, rawhide road!

My father came to Texas "to find room for his boys." There were eight of them. Other relatives soon followed. They settled the Bosque River Valley with plenty of space in between the ranch houses. Saturdays our place became a central gathering point where relatives and friends came to "stay all night." The children they brought along were almost as numerous as the prairie dogs on the roadside. While daylight lasted the boys played "one-eyed cat," "town ball," "stink-base" and "roley-holey." Sometimes the girls joined in the game of "Antny Over."

But after supper was over, the dishes washed and a roaring fire blazed in the kitchen fireplace, came the children's paradise. While the elders in an adjoining room gossiped, talked politics or crop prospects, the children played the quieter household games such as "club fist," "William-a-Trembletoe," "hull gull," "Jack in the bush" and many another. Later on, when the group had become more quiet, came the real battle of wits. How proud was the youngster who could bring a new puzzle or riddle in rhymed couplets that no one could solve. Each boy or girl, without any planning beforehand, was given a chance to make his contribution to the store of songs, jingles, rhymes, riddles or what not. Before the evening was over and the trundle beds drawn out and filled to overflowing, every child in the group had memorized what every other child knew. The group scattered after that week-end to teach other groups what they had learned. Thus these Saturday night gatherings became an important educational influence. These children lived in homes many of which were innocent of all books except, perhaps, the Bible. Their stock in trade, their mental stimulus in literature came on Saturday nights when they swapped rhymes and tunes with other eager listeners. All their literature was the spoken variety which Ray Wood is beginning to put together for us. This preliminary volume contains some of the best examples.

From the competitive spirit aroused by a group of youngsters, without doubt, came the creation of many of the items of this collection. Of course some of them have been imported, with or without change, from the British Empire, but many have the American tang, breathing the smoke and sweep of the border settlements.

> *"Possum up the gum stump,*
> *Cooney in the holler;*
> *Little girl at our house*
> *Fat as she can waller."*

Such a quatrain could emerge only from a home where the parents of "Little Girl" fed on plenty of hog jowl and lye-hominy, spare ribs, turnip greens and chitterlings. And this breed of men and women blazed the American frontier.

John A. Lomax.

CONTENTS

[xi]

[xii]

FOREWORD

In my boyhood in Arkansas, books, except those used in school, were hard to come by and that classic of child-lore, the Mother Goose Rhymes, was not known. The games, rhymes, riddles, etc., upon which we depended for amusement and entertainment were learned from parents or grand-parents who had received them in the same fashion.

Such rhymes as we did know of classic origin had been so changed by improvising to replace a forgotten line or to include some familiar scene or object that little remained of the original.

Most of the rhymes in this book were familiar to me from early childhood and have remained in

my memory, in whole or in fragments through-
out a half century of more serious but less endur-
ing interests, ideas, fads and philosophies.

The frequent recurrence to mind of these fool-
ish, jingling, little rhymes resulted in an urge to
collect and record them and in time this became
almost an obsession.

Everywhere I went I begged people to try to
recall for me the nonsense of their childhood.
Some of them plainly thought I was slightly "off-
center," but the majority showed a live sympathy.

Wealthy business men, famous authors and art-
ists, senators, congressmen and other nationally
known figures, newspaper writers, school teachers, poor hillside farmers and moonshiners and
their families all demonstrated a keen interest and
many supplied missing lines, their own variants
and some items I had not heard before.

I found that most of these items had been well known in all parts of the country with occasional variations of a word, a phrase or a line in New England, the Middle West or the Southern States, but many of them are known in exactly the same form everywhere in the country and still serve to entertain children of the present day both in the cities and in rural sections.

I showed my collection to John A. Lomax, who probably knows as much American folk-lore and has done as much to record and preserve it as any person alive. He looked it over and agreed it was the American Mother Goose.

I imagined pictures for these little jingles; pictures of the scenes in which I had first heard them. In searching for an artist to draw these pictures I came across Ed Hargis writing show cards in a clothing store in Beaumont, Tex. This talented youngster didn't have to be told. He had been born in the "piney woods" of East Texas and the scenes were as familiar to him as they were to me. We had a lot of fun.

I do not pretend to be able to trace the origin of these rhymes. Doubtless some of them did have their origin in the old country, but most of them seem to be of pure American invention. At any rate this is the Mother Goose I knew long before I ever heard of the classic. I still like it best.

Ray Wood.

Raywood, Texas,
March 12, 1940.

How much wood would a wood-chuck chuck
If a wood-chuck could chuck wood?
He would chuck as much wood as a wood-chuck
   would chuck,
If a wood-chuck could chuck wood.

Star-light, star-bright
First star I've seen tonight;
I wish I may, I wish I might
Get the wish I wish tonight.

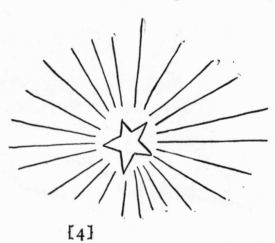

Fishy-fishy in the brook
    Daddy caught him with a hook;
Mammy fried him in the pan
    And baby ate him like a man.

Seven blackbirds in a tree,
Count them and see what they be.
One for sorrow
Two for joy
Three for a girl
Four for a boy;
Five for silver
Six for gold
Seven for a secret
that's never been told.

Mother may I go out to swim?
 Yes, my darling daughter,
But hang your clothes on a hickory limb
 And don't go near the water.

Sneeze on Monday,
Sneeze for danger.

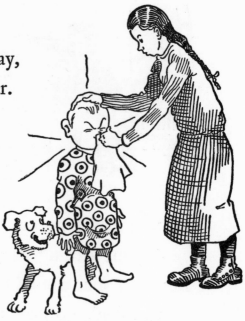

Sneeze on Tuesday,
Kiss a stranger.

[8]

Sneeze on Wednesday,
Sneeze for a letter.

Sneeze on Thursday,
Something better.

[9]

Sneeze on Friday,
Sneeze for sorrow.

Sneeze on Saturday,
Joy tomorrow.

Sneeze on Sunday,
Company comin'.

There was an owl lived in an oak
The more he heard the less he spoke;
The less he spoke the more he heard—
Good children should be like that bird.

Obadiah
Jumped in the fire,

Fire was so hot
He jumped in the pot,

The pot was so little
He jumped in the kettle,

The kettle was so black
He jumped in the crack,

The crack was so high
He jumped to the sky,

The sky was so blue
He jumped in the canoe,

The canoe was so deep
He jumped in the creek,

The creek was so shallow
He jumped in the tallow,

The tallow was so hard
He jumped in the lard,

The lard was so soft
He jumped in the loft,

The loft was so rotten
He fell in the cotton,

The cotton was so white
He took off his shoes
and stayed all night.

[15]

Bat, bat, come under my hat
And I'll give you a slice of bacon,
And when I bake, I'll give you a cake,
If I am not mistaken.

Good-night
Sleep tight
Don't let the mosquitoes bite.

Goosey–Goosey–Gander
Who stands yonder?
Little Betsy Baker,
Pick her up and shake her.

I asked my mother for fifteen cents
To see the elephant jump the fence,
He jumped so high that he touched the sky
And never came back 'till the Fourth of July.

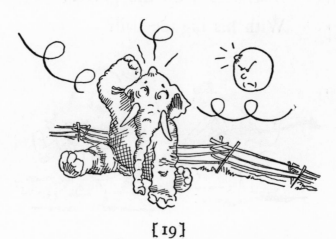

Did you ever see the devil
With his iron spade and shovel
A-scratchin' up the gravel
With his big-toe nail?

Monkey on the railroad,
Monkey on the fence,
Monkey get your hair cut—
Fifteen cents.
Monkey in the barnyard,
Monkey in the stable,
Monkey get your hair cut
Soon as you are able.

Ninety-nine men in a boarding-house bed
    Turn Over, Turn Over
They'd all turn over when one of them spoke
    Turn Over, Turn Over
One of them thought he would play a good joke
He wouldn't turn over when the other one spoke
And in the shuffle his neck was broke
    Turn Over, Turn Over.

I went to the river
And couldn't get across,
Paid five dollars
For an old gray hoss.

The horse wouldn't pull,
So I traded for a bull;

The bull wouldn't holler,
So I traded for a dollar;

The dollar wouldn't pass,
So I throwed it in the grass;

The grass wouldn't grow,
So I traded for a hoe;

The hoe wouldn't dig,
So I traded for a pig;

[25]

The pig wouldn't squeal,
So I traded for a wheel;

The wheel wouldn't run,
So I traded for a gun;

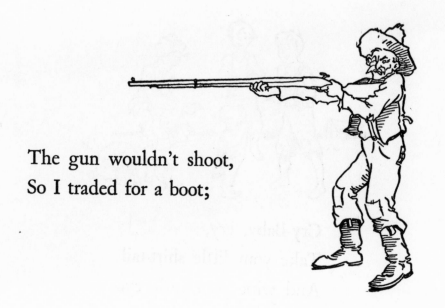

The gun wouldn't shoot,
So I traded for a boot;

The boot wouldn't fit,
So I thought I'd better quit.

[27]

Cry-Baby, cry,
Take your little shirt-tail
And wipe your little eye
And go tell your mammy
To give you a piece of pie.

Old man Persnicketty
Ran down the lane
With a shirt-tail full of hominy
And never lost a grain.

Leather britches, full of stitches,
Mammy sewed the buttons on,
And Daddy kicked me out of bed
Because I had my britches on.

All I need to make me happy
Two little boys to call me pappy,
One named Biscuit t'other named Gravy—
If I had another'n I'd call him Davy.

Jaybird a settin' on a swingin' limb,
He winked at me–I winked at him;
I picked up a rock and skinned his shin;
Says he, "Old feller, don't do that again!"

Snake baked a hoe-cake,
    And set the frog to mind it;
Frog went to sleep
    And the lizard come and found it.

Mary had a little lamb,
   Its fleece was white as cotton,
And everywhere that Mary went
   The lamb it went a-trottin'.

Somebody stole our big black dog
And we said to bring him back.
He run the big hogs over the fence
And the little ones through the crack.

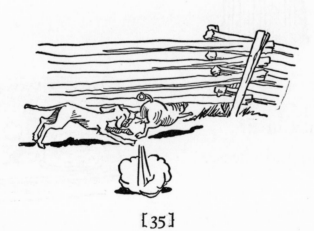

Club Fist!
Take it off or
        I'll knock it off.

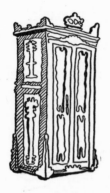

What you got there?
The King's Cupboard.

What's in it?
Bread and cheese.

Where's my share?
The cat's got it.

Where's the cat?
In the woods.

Where's the woods?
The fire burnt it.

Where's the fire?
The water quenched it.

Where's the water?
The ox drank it.

Where's the ox?
The butcher killed it.

Where's the butcher?
The rope hung him.

Where's the rope?
The knife cut it.

Where's the knife?
The hammer broke it.

Where's the hammer?
Out behind the barn
Cracking hickory nuts.

Listen, listen and you shall hear
How the old cow died with a bug in her ear.
The bug flew out, the wind blew in,
The old cow's up and gone again.

Green corn, green corn,
Fotch along a jimmy-john;
Fat meat, fat meat,
That's what the Injuns eat.

Hippity-hop to the barber shop
To get a stick of candy,
One for you and one for me
And one for Sister Mandy.

Left foot, right foot,
Any foot at all,
Sally lost her petticoat
A-goin' to the ball.

Skinner–Skinner–don't you know the rule?
Get up in the morning and harness your mule,
Get up in the morning soon, soon;
You can't see nothing but the stars and the moon.

Chicken in the bread-pan,
Pickin' up the dough;
Granny will your dog bite?
No, child, no.

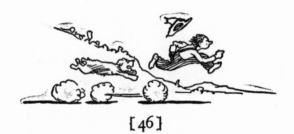

One, Two
Buckle my shoe

Three, Four
Shut the door

Five, Six
Pick up sticks

Seven, Eight
Lay them straight

[48]

Nine, Ten
A big fat hen

Eleven, Twelve
Cook it well

[49]

Thirteen, Fourteen
Boys a-courting

Fifteen, Sixteen
Girls a'fixing

Seventeen, Eighteen
Girls a-waiting

Nineteen, Twenty
Girls a-plenty

Had a little pony,
His name was Jack;
Put him in the stable
And he jumped through a crack.
Picked up a cob
And knocked him back—
Whoa, Jack!

A trout and a shad spells Nebuchad,
A strap and a razor spells Nebuchadnezzer;
My old stockings and your old shoes
Spells Nebuchadnezzer, the King of the Jews.

Workin' on the turn-pike,
Fifty cents a day,
Shovelin' up gravel
And throwin' it away.

If I don't get crippled,
And I don't get killed,
I'll be workin' here tomorrow
On the same old hill.

Peckerwood a-settin' on a swingin' limb,
Blue-bird a-buildin' in the garden,
Old gray goose a-settin' in the lane
And a'hatchin' on the other side of Jordan.

Possum up a gum stump,
Coonie in the holler,
Wake, Snake! June Bug
Stole a half a dollar.

William Tremble-toe is a good fisherman
Catches fish—puts them in a dish;
Catches hens—puts them in pens;
Some lay eggs—some lay none.
Wire, briar, limberlock, three geese in a flock,
One flew east, one flew west,
One flew over the cuckoo's nest.

Goody-Goody-Gout,
Your shirt tail's out,
Goody-Goody-Gin,
You better stick it in.

I'll eat when I'm hungry
And drink when I'm dry.
If a tree don't fall on me,
I'll live 'till I die.

A little old man came riding by
Says I, "Old man, your horse will die."
"Well, if he does I'll tan his skin,
And if he lives I'll ride him again."

Hokey–Pokey,
Hanky–Panky,
I'm the King of Rankee-Jankee
And I'm well, I thank ye.

Tommy was a man of law,
He sold his bed to lie on straw;
He sold the straw to lie on grass,
To buy his wife a looking glass.

Hush my baby,
    don't say a word,
Daddy'll buy you
    a mocking bird.

When that mocking bird won't sing,
Daddy'll buy you a diamond ring.

When that diamond ring turns to brass,
Daddy'll buy you a looking glass.

When that looking glass gets broke,
Daddy'll buy you a billy goat.

When that billy goat gets bony,
Daddy'll buy you a shetland pony.

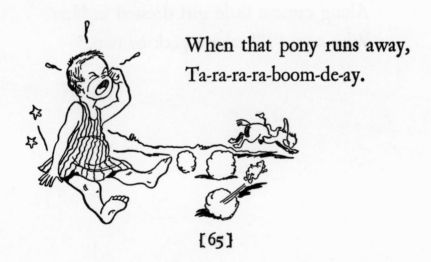

When that pony runs away,
Ta-ra-ra-ra-boom-de-ay.

[65]

The boy stood on the burning deck
Selling peanuts by the peck,
Along came a little girl dressed in blue
Who says, "I'll take a peck or two."

Jay bird, Jay bird, settin' on a rail,
Pickin' his teeth with the end of his tail,
Mulberry leaves and calico sleeves
All school teachers are hard to please.

Had a little dog, his name was Rover,
When he died he died all over,
All but his tail and it turned over
Over and over and ten times over.

Ding-Dong-Davy
Daddy shot a bear,
Shot him full of buckshot
And never touched a hair.

P-U-N-kin,
N-kin-Y,
Double-E-N-kin,
Pumpkin Pie.

There was an old man named Michael Finnegan,
He grew a long beard right on his chinnigan,
Along came a wind and blew it in again—
Poor old Michael Finnegan.

Wake me! Shake me!
Don't let me sleep too late,
Wake me early in the morning
To swing on the Golden Gate.

Hound dog in the dinner pot,
  Lick, lick, lick,
Chicken in the bread tray,
  Pick, pick, pick.

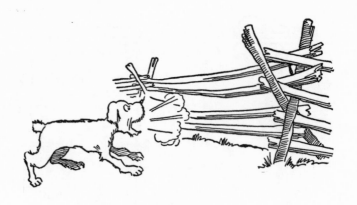

Had a little dog
He had no sense,
Ran under the house
And barked at the fence.

Had a mule his name was Jack
   I rode his tail to save his back;
His tail got loose and I fell back—
   Whoa Jack!

When I am the president of these United States
I'll eat molasses candy and swing on all the gates.

See one buzzard, don't see two
You'll see someone you're not expecting to.

P with a little o,
S with a t,
O double f,
And i-c-e-

I wish I was a little rock a-settin' on a hill,
  A-doin' nothin' all day long but just a-settin'
  still.
I wouldn't eat, I wouldn't sleep, I wouldn't
  even wash,
  I'd just sit there the whole day long and rest
  myself by gosh!

Doodle-bug, doodle-bug,
Home you must fly
Your house is on fire
And your children will die.

Pretty little red-bird,
Dressed so fine,
Got a little red coat
Just like mine.

Barley-corn, barley-corn, Injun-meal shorts,
Spunk-water, spunk-water, swaller these warts.

One, two, three,
Towser caught a flea;
Four, five, six,
Towser caught a tick;
Eight, nine, ten,
They got away again.

God made man and man made money,
God made bees and bees made honey,
God made the hog and the hog made meat,
Good hog and hominy is hard to beat.

RIDDLES

Eyes it has yet cannot see,
Tongue, but cannot speak to me;
And although it's well-behaved
Has a sole that can't be saved.

In summer it dies,
 In winter it grows,
Its roots above,
 Its head below.

There was a girl lived in our town,
Silk an' satin was her gown,
Silk an' satin, gold an' velvet.
Now guess her name, three times I've telled it.

It always runs.　It never walks.
It has a tongue but never talks.
It's always tired, but never sleeps.
Its bed above its body keeps.

Runs all day and never walks,
Often murmurs, never talks.
It has a bed but never sleeps,
It has a mouth, but never eats.

I have a little sister they call her "Peep-peep,"
She wades in the ocean deep, deep, deep.
She climbs up the mountain high, high, high,
The poor little thing hasn't got but one eye.

Adam and Eve and Pinch-me-tight.
Went over the river to see the fight.
Adam and Eve came back before night,
Now who was left to see the fight?

A houseful, a hole full,
Yet couldn't catch a bowlful.

Three legs up as hard as stone,
Two legs down with meat on the bone,
Two ears living and two ears dead,
Tell me the riddle and I'll give you the head.

GAMES

AND

FINGER PLAYS

One for the money,
Two for the show,
Three to make ready,
Four to go.

Eerie, oarie, eekerie, Ann,
Fillison, follison, Nicholas, John,
Queavy, quavy, English navy,
Sticklum, stacklum Buck.

We're marching
  round the levee,
We're marching
  round the levee,
We're marching
  round the levee,
And I hope we'll
  gain the day.

Go in and out
  the windows,
Go in and out
  the windows,
Go in and out
  the windows,
And I hope we'll
  gain the day.

Go forth and choose
    your lover,
Go forth and choose
    your lover,
Go forth and choose
    your lover,
And I hope we'll
    gain the day.

I measure my love
    to show you,
I measure my love
    to show you,
I measure my love
    to show you,
And I hope we'll
    gain the day.

I kneel because
    I love you,
I kneel because
    I love you,
I kneel because
    I love you,
And I hope we'll
    gain the day.

Boo-hoo, I hate
    to leave you,
Boo-hoo, I hate
    to leave you,
Boo-hoo, I hate
    to leave you,
And I hope we'll
    gain the day.

Green gravel, green gravel, the grass is so green
And all the young maidens ashamed to be seen
Dear Mary, dear Mary, your true love is dead
He sent you a letter to turn back your head.

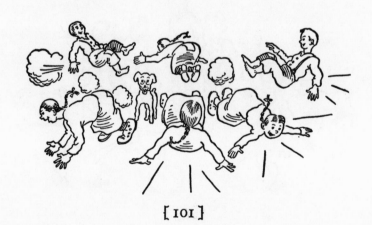

Ring around the rosie,
    A pocket full of posies,
Every body squat—
    Then up jumps Josie.

Bushel of wheat, bushel of rye
All that ain't hid, holler out "aye"

Bushel of wheat, bushel of clover,
All that ain't hid, can't hide over.

Eye winker,
Brow blinker,
Nose crooker,
Lip lopper,
Chin chopper,
Gulley,
Gully,
Gully.

Thirty-two white calves
Stand on a hill,
Up comes a red cow
And licks over all.

Round as a biscuit,
Busy as a bee,
Prettiest little thing
You ever did see.

Here's the church,
There's the steeple,
Open the door
And see all the people.

This is mother's
looking glass

And this is
baby's cradle,

These are mother's
knives and forks,

This is mother's
table.